horse

goat

alpaca

cockerel

sheep

sheepdog

llama

Pet animals

dog

cockatoo

mouse

ferret

chameleon

goldfish

tortoise

guinea pig

tropical fish

hamster

rabbit

canary

budgerigar

Shetland pony

cat

In the woods

frog

badger

woodpecker

pheasant

tawny owl

slug

butterfly

woodlouse

hedgehog

deer

spider

bat

dragonfly

red fox

squirrel

Under the sea

clownfish

seahorse

starfish

turtle

shark

lobster

octopus

puffer fish

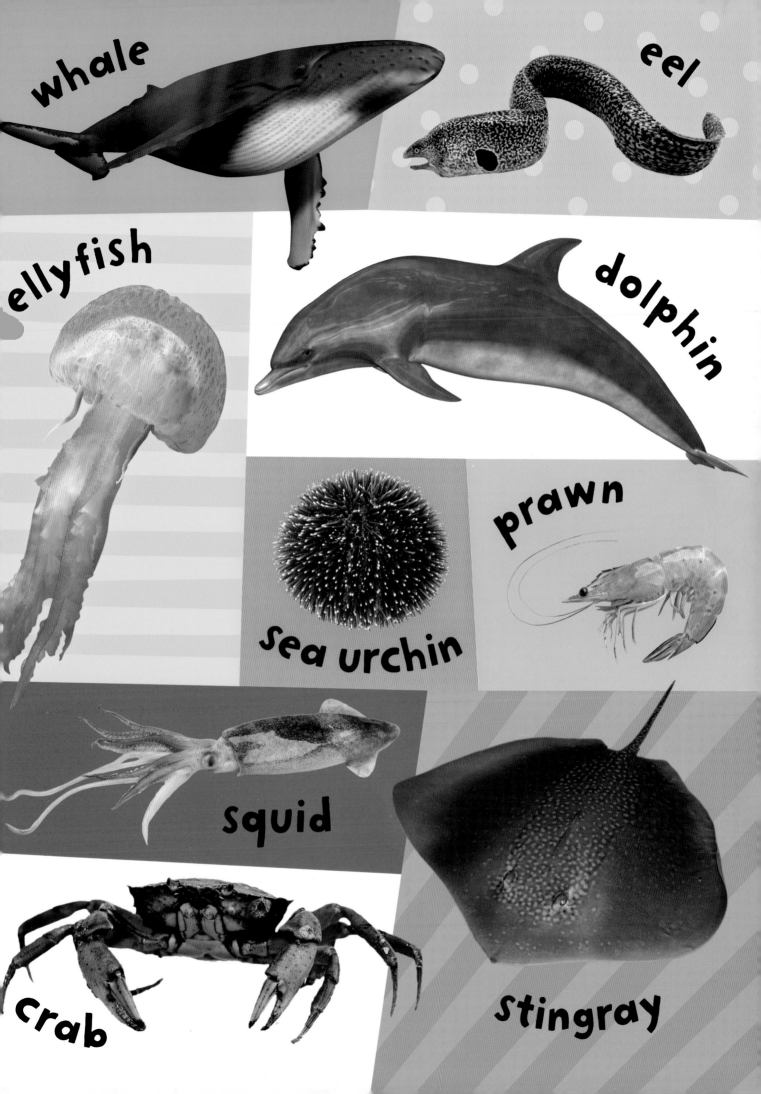

whale

eel

ellyfish

dolphin

sea urchin

prawn

squid

stingray

crab

In the cold

snowy owl

polar bear

grizzly bear

musk ox

reindeer

Arctic fox

harp seal

snow leopard

penguin

Arctic hare

wolf

puffin

walrus

Desert and bush

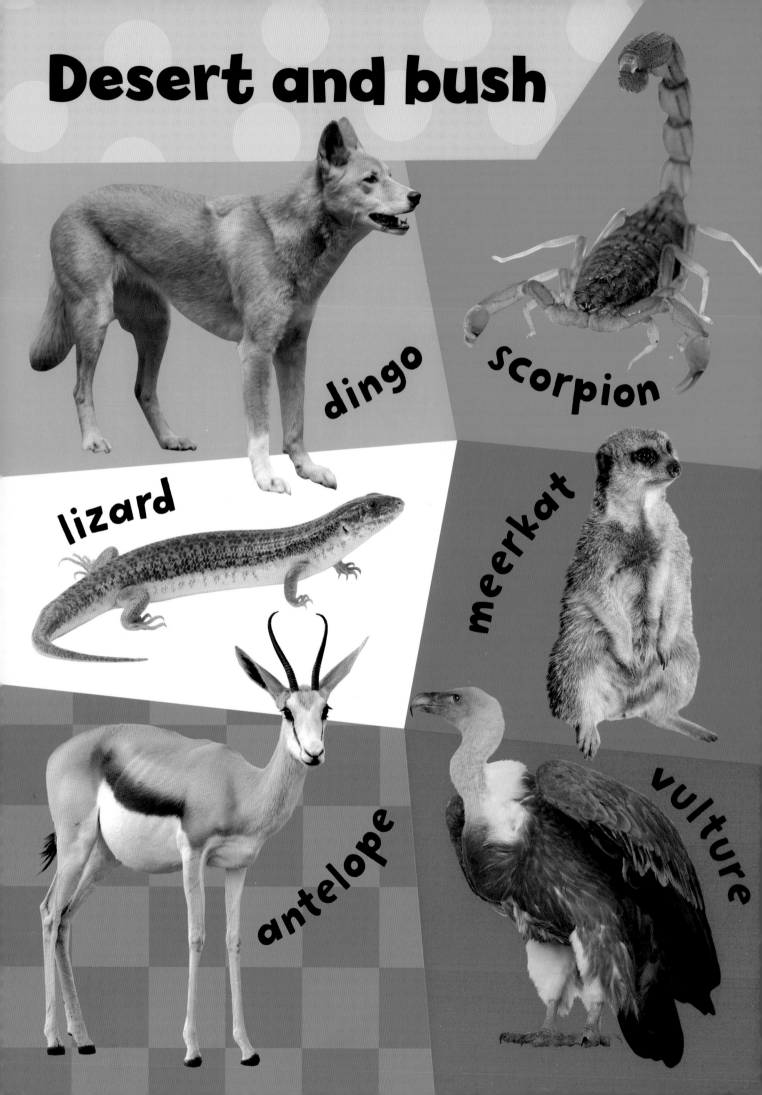

dingo

scorpion

lizard

meerkat

antelope

vulture

koala

ostrich

kangaroo

skunk

camel

snake

On safari

parrot

tiger

rhinoceros

lion

leopard

zebra

hippopotamus